How To Use Your Low FODMAP Food Diary

Keeping track of your food intake each day is a great way to help you track down what foods are causing your IBS problems.

Write down each meal and snack you consume as well as any symptoms that you notice. Keep track of your water intake by putting a cross on each glass of water - each one represents roughly an 8oz glass. Be sure to make note of any thing that comes to mind in the notes section and add your goals for the day or week.

At the end of the diary there is a table where you can note down all the foods that you have found you can tolerate and ones which are causing you symptoms.

Using this diary is a great tool to help you feel better and make dealing with food intolerances a little easier. We wish you great health!

Food Diary

Date _____

	Food and Drink	Symptoms and Notes
Breakfast		
Snack		
Lunch		
Snack		
Dinner		
Snack		

Notes and Goals

Water

Food Diary

Date _____

	Food and Drink	Symptoms and Notes
Breakfast		
Snack		
Lunch		
Snack		
Dinner		
Snack		

Notes and Goals

Water

Food Diary

Date _____

	Food and Drink	Symptoms and Notes
Breakfast		
Snack		
Lunch		
Snack		
Dinner		
Snack		

Notes and Goals

Water

Food Diary

Date _____

	Food and Drink	Symptoms and Notes
Breakfast		
Snack		
Lunch		
Snack		
Dinner		
Snack		

Notes and Goals

Water

Food Diary

Date _____

	Food and Drink	Symptoms and Notes
Breakfast		
Snack		
Lunch		
Snack		
Dinner		
Snack		

Notes and Goals

Water

Food Diary

Date _____

	Food and Drink	Symptoms and Notes
Breakfast		
Snack		
Lunch		
Snack		
Dinner		
Snack		

Notes and Goals

Water

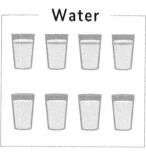

Food Diary

	Food and Drink	Symptoms and Notes
Breakfast		
Snack		
Lunch		
Snack		
Dinner		
Snack		

Notes and Goals

Water

Food Diary

Date _____

	Food and Drink	Symptoms and Notes
Breakfast		
Snack		
Lunch		
Snack		
Dinner		
Snack		

Notes and Goals

Water

Food Diary

Date _____

	Food and Drink	Symptoms and Notes
Breakfast		
Snack		
Lunch		
Snack		
Dinner		
Snack		

Notes and Goals

Water

Food Diary

Date _____

	Food and Drink	Symptoms and Notes
Breakfast		
Snack		
Lunch		
Snack		
Dinner		
Snack		

Notes and Goals

Water

Food Diary

Date _____

	Food and Drink	Symptoms and Notes
Breakfast		
Snack		
Lunch		
Snack		
Dinner		
Snack		

Notes and Goals

Water

Food Diary

Date _____

	Food and Drink	Symptoms and Notes
Breakfast		
Snack		
Lunch		
Snack		
Dinner		
Snack		

Notes and Goals

Water

Food Diary

Date _____

	Food and Drink	Symptoms and Notes
Breakfast		
Snack		
Lunch		
Snack		
Dinner		
Snack		

Notes and Goals

Water

Food Diary

Date _____

	Food and Drink	Symptoms and Notes
Breakfast		
Snack		
Lunch		
Snack		
Dinner		
Snack		

Notes and Goals

Water

Food Diary

Date _____

	Food and Drink	Symptoms and Notes
Breakfast		
Snack		
Lunch		
Snack		
Dinner		
Snack		

Notes and Goals

Water

Food Diary

Date _____

	Food and Drink	Symptoms and Notes
Breakfast		
Snack		
Lunch		
Snack		
Dinner		
Snack		

Notes and Goals

Water

Food Diary

Date _____

	Food and Drink	Symptoms and Notes
Breakfast		
Snack		
Lunch		
Snack		
Dinner		
Snack		

Notes and Goals

Water

Food Diary

Date _____

	Food and Drink	Symptoms and Notes
Breakfast		
Snack		
Lunch		
Snack		
Dinner		
Snack		

Notes and Goals

Water

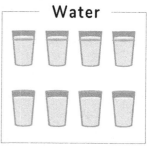

Food Diary

Date _____

	Food and Drink	Symptoms and Notes
Breakfast		
Snack		
Lunch		
Snack		
Dinner		
Snack		

Notes and Goals

Water

Food Diary

Date _____

	Food and Drink	Symptoms and Notes
Breakfast		
Snack		
Lunch		
Snack		
Dinner		
Snack		

Notes and Goals

Water

Food Diary

Date _____

	Food and Drink	Symptoms and Notes
Breakfast		
Snack		
Lunch		
Snack		
Dinner		
Snack		

Notes and Goals

Water

Food Diary

Date _____

	Food and Drink	Symptoms and Notes
Breakfast		
Snack		
Lunch		
Snack		
Dinner		
Snack		

Notes and Goals

Water

Food Diary

Date _____

	Food and Drink	Symptoms and Notes
Breakfast		
Snack		
Lunch		
Snack		
Dinner		
Snack		

Notes and Goals

Water

Food Diary

Date _____

	Food and Drink	Symptoms and Notes
Breakfast		
Snack		
Lunch		
Snack		
Dinner		
Snack		

Notes and Goals

Water

Food Diary

Date _____

	Food and Drink	Symptoms and Notes
Breakfast		
Snack		
Lunch		
Snack		
Dinner		
Snack		

Notes and Goals

Water

Food Diary

Date _____

	Food and Drink	Symptoms and Notes
Breakfast		
Snack		
Lunch		
Snack		
Dinner		
Snack		

Notes and Goals

Water

Food Diary

Date _____

	Food and Drink	Symptoms and Notes
Breakfast		
Snack		
Lunch		
Snack		
Dinner		
Snack		

Notes and Goals

Water

Food Diary

Date _____

	Food and Drink	Symptoms and Notes
Breakfast		
Snack		
Lunch		
Snack		
Dinner		
Snack		

Notes and Goals

Water

Food Diary

Date _____

	Food and Drink	Symptoms and Notes
Breakfast		
Snack		
Lunch		
Snack		
Dinner		
Snack		

Notes and Goals

Water

Food Diary

Date _____

	Food and Drink	Symptoms and Notes
Breakfast		
Snack		
Lunch		
Snack		
Dinner		
Snack		

Notes and Goals

Water

Food Diary

Date _____

	Food and Drink	Symptoms and Notes
Breakfast		
Snack		
Lunch		
Snack		
Dinner		
Snack		

Notes and Goals

Water

Food Diary

Date _____

	Food and Drink	Symptoms and Notes
Breakfast		
Snack		
Lunch		
Snack		
Dinner		
Snack		

Notes and Goals

Water

Food Diary

Date _____

	Food and Drink	Symptoms and Notes
Breakfast		
Snack		
Lunch		
Snack		
Dinner		
Snack		

Notes and Goals

Water

Food Diary

Date _____

	Food and Drink	Symptoms and Notes
Breakfast		
Snack		
Lunch		
Snack		
Dinner		
Snack		

Notes and Goals

Water

Food Diary

Date _____

	Food and Drink	Symptoms and Notes
Breakfast		
Snack		
Lunch		
Snack		
Dinner		
Snack		

Notes and Goals

Water

Food Diary

Date _____

	Food and Drink	Symptoms and Notes
Breakfast		
Snack		
Lunch		
Snack		
Dinner		
Snack		

Notes and Goals

Water

Food Diary

Date _____

	Food and Drink	Symptoms and Notes
Breakfast		
Snack		
Lunch		
Snack		
Dinner		
Snack		

Notes and Goals

Water

Food Diary

Date _____

	Food and Drink	Symptoms and Notes
Breakfast		
Snack		
Lunch		
Snack		
Dinner		
Snack		

Notes and Goals

Water

Food Diary

Date _____

	Food and Drink	Symptoms and Notes
Breakfast		
Snack		
Lunch		
Snack		
Dinner		
Snack		

Notes and Goals

Water

Food Diary

Date _____

	Food and Drink	Symptoms and Notes
Breakfast		
Snack		
Lunch		
Snack		
Dinner		
Snack		

Notes and Goals

Water

Food Diary

Date _____

	Food and Drink	Symptoms and Notes
Breakfast		
Snack		
Lunch		
Snack		
Dinner		
Snack		

Notes and Goals

Water

Food Diary

Date _____

	Food and Drink	Symptoms and Notes
Breakfast		
Snack		
Lunch		
Snack		
Dinner		
Snack		

Notes and Goals

Water

Food Diary

Date _____

	Food and Drink	Symptoms and Notes
Breakfast		
Snack		
Lunch		
Snack		
Dinner		
Snack		

Notes and Goals

Water

Food Diary

Date _____

	Food and Drink	Symptoms and Notes
Breakfast		
Snack		
Lunch		
Snack		
Dinner		
Snack		

Notes and Goals

Water

Food Diary

Date _____

	Food and Drink	Symptoms and Notes
Breakfast		
Snack		
Lunch		
Snack		
Dinner		
Snack		

Notes and Goals

Water

Food Diary

Date _____

	Food and Drink	Symptoms and Notes
Breakfast		
Snack		
Lunch		
Snack		
Dinner		
Snack		

Notes and Goals

Water

Food Diary

Date _____

	Food and Drink	Symptoms and Notes
Breakfast		
Snack		
Lunch		
Snack		
Dinner		
Snack		

Notes and Goals

Water

Food Diary

Date _____

	Food and Drink	Symptoms and Notes
Breakfast		
Snack		
Lunch		
Snack		
Dinner		
Snack		

Notes and Goals

Water

Food Diary

Date _____

	Food and Drink	Symptoms and Notes
Breakfast		
Snack		
Lunch		
Snack		
Dinner		
Snack		

Notes and Goals

Water

Food Diary

Date _____

	Food and Drink	Symptoms and Notes
Breakfast		
Snack		
Lunch		
Snack		
Dinner		
Snack		

Notes and Goals

Water

Food Diary

Date _____

	Food and Drink	Symptoms and Notes
Breakfast		
Snack		
Lunch		
Snack		
Dinner		
Snack		

Notes and Goals

Water

Food Diary

Date _____

	Food and Drink	Symptoms and Notes
Breakfast		
Snack		
Lunch		
Snack		
Dinner		
Snack		

Notes and Goals

Water

Food Diary

Date _____

	Food and Drink	Symptoms and Notes
Breakfast		
Snack		
Lunch		
Snack		
Dinner		
Snack		

Notes and Goals

Water

Food Diary

Date _____

	Food and Drink	Symptoms and Notes
Breakfast		
Snack		
Lunch		
Snack		
Dinner		
Snack		

Notes and Goals

Water

Food Diary

Date _____

	Food and Drink	Symptoms and Notes
Breakfast		
Snack		
Lunch		
Snack		
Dinner		
Snack		

Notes and Goals

Water

Food Diary

Date _____

	Food and Drink	Symptoms and Notes
Breakfast		
Snack		
Lunch		
Snack		
Dinner		
Snack		

Notes and Goals

Water

Food Diary

Date _____

	Food and Drink	Symptoms and Notes
Breakfast		
Snack		
Lunch		
Snack		
Dinner		
Snack		

Notes and Goals

Water

Food Diary

Date _____

	Food and Drink	Symptoms and Notes
Breakfast		
Snack		
Lunch		
Snack		
Dinner		
Snack		

Notes and Goals

Water

Food Diary

Date _____

	Food and Drink	Symptoms and Notes
Breakfast		
Snack		
Lunch		
Snack		
Dinner		
Snack		

Notes and Goals

Water

Food Diary

Date _____

	Food and Drink	Symptoms and Notes
Breakfast		
Snack		
Lunch		
Snack		
Dinner		
Snack		

Notes and Goals

Water

Food Diary

Date _____

	Food and Drink	Symptoms and Notes
Breakfast		
Snack		
Lunch		
Snack		
Dinner		
Snack		

Notes and Goals

Water

Food Diary

Date _____

	Food and Drink	Symptoms and Notes
Breakfast		
Snack		
Lunch		
Snack		
Dinner		
Snack		

Notes and Goals

Water

Food Diary

Date _____

	Food and Drink	Symptoms and Notes
Breakfast		
Snack		
Lunch		
Snack		
Dinner		
Snack		

Notes and Goals

Water

Food Diary

Date _____

	Food and Drink	Symptoms and Notes
Breakfast		
Snack		
Lunch		
Snack		
Dinner		
Snack		

Notes and Goals

Water

Food Diary

Date _____

	Food and Drink	Symptoms and Notes
Breakfast		
Snack		
Lunch		
Snack		
Dinner		
Snack		

Notes and Goals

Water

Food Diary

Date _____

	Food and Drink	Symptoms and Notes
Breakfast		
Snack		
Lunch		
Snack		
Dinner		
Snack		

Notes and Goals

Water

Food Diary

Date _____

	Food and Drink	Symptoms and Notes
Breakfast		
Snack		
Lunch		
Snack		
Dinner		
Snack		

Notes and Goals

Water

Food Diary

Date _____

	Food and Drink	Symptoms and Notes
Breakfast		
Snack		
Lunch		
Snack		
Dinner		
Snack		

Notes and Goals

Water

Food Diary

Date _____

	Food and Drink	Symptoms and Notes
Breakfast		
Snack		
Lunch		
Snack		
Dinner		
Snack		

Notes and Goals

Water

Food Diary

Date _____

	Food and Drink	Symptoms and Notes
Breakfast		
Snack		
Lunch		
Snack		
Dinner		
Snack		

Notes and Goals

Water

Food Diary

Date _____

	Food and Drink	Symptoms and Notes
Breakfast		
Snack		
Lunch		
Snack		
Dinner		
Snack		

Notes and Goals

Water

Food Diary

Date _____

	Food and Drink	Symptoms and Notes
Breakfast		
Snack		
Lunch		
Snack		
Dinner		
Snack		

Notes and Goals

Water

Food Diary

Date _____

	Food and Drink	Symptoms and Notes
Breakfast		
Snack		
Lunch		
Snack		
Dinner		
Snack		

Notes and Goals

Water

Food Diary

Date _____

	Food and Drink	Symptoms and Notes
Breakfast		
Snack		
Lunch		
Snack		
Dinner		
Snack		

Notes and Goals

Water

Food Diary

Date _____

	Food and Drink	Symptoms and Notes
Breakfast		
Snack		
Lunch		
Snack		
Dinner		
Snack		

Notes and Goals

Water

Food Diary

Date _____

	Food and Drink	Symptoms and Notes
Breakfast		
Snack		
Lunch		
Snack		
Dinner		
Snack		

Notes and Goals

Water

Food Diary

Date _____

	Food and Drink	Symptoms and Notes
Breakfast		
Snack		
Lunch		
Snack		
Dinner		
Snack		

Notes and Goals

Water

Food Diary

Date _____

	Food and Drink	Symptoms and Notes
Breakfast		
Snack		
Lunch		
Snack		
Dinner		
Snack		

Notes and Goals

Water

Food Diary

Date _____

	Food and Drink	Symptoms and Notes
Breakfast		
Snack		
Lunch		
Snack		
Dinner		
Snack		

Notes and Goals

Water

Food Diary

Date _____

	Food and Drink	Symptoms and Notes
Breakfast		
Snack		
Lunch		
Snack		
Dinner		
Snack		

Notes and Goals

Water

Food Diary

Date _____

	Food and Drink	Symptoms and Notes
Breakfast		
Snack		
Lunch		
Snack		
Dinner		
Snack		

Notes and Goals

Water

Food Diary

Date _____

	Food and Drink	Symptoms and Notes
Breakfast		
Snack		
Lunch		
Snack		
Dinner		
Snack		

Notes and Goals

Water

Food Diary

Date _____

	Food and Drink	Symptoms and Notes
Breakfast		
Snack		
Lunch		
Snack		
Dinner		
Snack		

Notes and Goals

Water

Food Diary

Date _____

	Food and Drink	Symptoms and Notes
Breakfast		
Snack		
Lunch		
Snack		
Dinner		
Snack		

Notes and Goals

Water

Food Diary

Date _____

	Food and Drink	Symptoms and Notes
Breakfast		
Snack		
Lunch		
Snack		
Dinner		
Snack		

Notes and Goals

Water

Food Diary

Date _____

	Food and Drink	Symptoms and Notes
Breakfast		
Snack		
Lunch		
Snack		
Dinner		
Snack		

Notes and Goals

Water

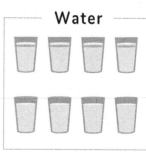

Food Diary

Date _____

	Food and Drink	Symptoms and Notes
Breakfast		
Snack		
Lunch		
Snack		
Dinner		
Snack		

Notes and Goals

Water

Food Diary

Date _____

	Food and Drink	Symptoms and Notes
Breakfast		
Snack		
Lunch		
Snack		
Dinner		
Snack		

Notes and Goals

Water

Food Diary

Date _____

	Food and Drink	Symptoms and Notes
Breakfast		
Snack		
Lunch		
Snack		
Dinner		
Snack		

Notes and Goals

Water

Food Diary

Date _____

	Food and Drink	Symptoms and Notes
Breakfast		
Snack		
Lunch		
Snack		
Dinner		
Snack		

Notes and Goals

Water

Food Diary

Date _____

	Food and Drink	Symptoms and Notes
Breakfast		
Snack		
Lunch		
Snack		
Dinner		
Snack		

Notes and Goals

Water

Food Diary

Date _____

	Food and Drink	Symptoms and Notes
Breakfast		
Snack		
Lunch		
Snack		
Dinner		
Snack		

Notes and Goals

Water

Food Diary

Date _____

	Food and Drink	Symptoms and Notes
Breakfast		
Snack		
Lunch		
Snack		
Dinner		
Snack		

Notes and Goals

Water

Food Diary

Date _____

	Food and Drink	Symptoms and Notes
Breakfast		
Snack		
Lunch		
Snack		
Dinner		
Snack		

Notes and Goals

Water

Food Diary

Date _____

	Food and Drink	Symptoms and Notes
Breakfast		
Snack		
Lunch		
Snack		
Dinner		
Snack		

Notes and Goals

Water

Food Diary

Date _____

	Food and Drink	Symptoms and Notes
Breakfast		
Snack		
Lunch		
Snack		
Dinner		
Snack		

Notes and Goals

Water

Food Diary

Date _____

	Food and Drink	Symptoms and Notes
Breakfast		
Snack		
Lunch		
Snack		
Dinner		
Snack		

Notes and Goals

Water

Food Diary

Date _____

	Food and Drink	Symptoms and Notes
Breakfast		
Snack		
Lunch		
Snack		
Dinner		
Snack		

Notes and Goals

Water

Food Diary

Date _____

	Food and Drink	Symptoms and Notes
Breakfast		
Snack		
Lunch		
Snack		
Dinner		
Snack		

Notes and Goals

Water

Food Diary

Date _____

	Food and Drink	Symptoms and Notes
Breakfast		
Snack		
Lunch		
Snack		
Dinner		
Snack		

Notes and Goals

Water

Food Diary

Date _____

	Food and Drink	Symptoms and Notes
Breakfast		
Snack		
Lunch		
Snack		
Dinner		
Snack		

Notes and Goals

Water

Food Diary

Date _____

	Food and Drink	Symptoms and Notes
Breakfast		
Snack		
Lunch		
Snack		
Dinner		
Snack		

Notes and Goals

Water

Food Diary

Date _____

	Food and Drink	Symptoms and Notes
Breakfast		
Snack		
Lunch		
Snack		
Dinner		
Snack		

Notes and Goals

Water

Food Diary

Date _____

	Food and Drink	Symptoms and Notes
Breakfast		
Snack		
Lunch		
Snack		
Dinner		
Snack		

Notes and Goals

Water

Food Diary

Date _____

	Food and Drink	Symptoms and Notes
Breakfast		
Snack		
Lunch		
Snack		
Dinner		
Snack		

Notes and Goals

Water

Food Diary

Date _____

	Food and Drink	Symptoms and Notes
Breakfast		
Snack		
Lunch		
Snack		
Dinner		
Snack		

Notes and Goals

Water

Good Foods	Bad Foods

Good Foods	Bad Foods

Good Foods	Bad Foods

Good Foods	Bad Foods

Good Foods	Bad Foods

Good Foods	Bad Foods

Good Foods	Bad Foods

Good Foods	Bad Foods

Good Foods	Bad Foods

Good Foods	Bad Foods